For David, Christine and Ian.
A wonderful godson
and special friends.

Neil x

Red Robin Books is an imprint of Corner To Learn Limited

Published by

Corner To Learn Limited

Willow Cottage • 26 Purton Stoke • Swindon • Wiltshire SN5 4JF • UK

ISBN: 978-1-908702-04-3

First published in the UK 2012

Text © Neil Griffiths 2012, Illustrations © Peggy Collins 2012

Design and paper engineering by

David Rose

Printed in China

The Pelican who couldn't

Neil Griffiths

Illustrated by **Peggy Collins**

Two pelicans were sitting
on a rock together,
looking eagerly out to sea.

One said to the other,
"I could eat that whole school
of pilchards in one go!"
"But they will tickle and wriggle,"
replied the other pelican.
"Well, I still can."

And guess what!
It could!

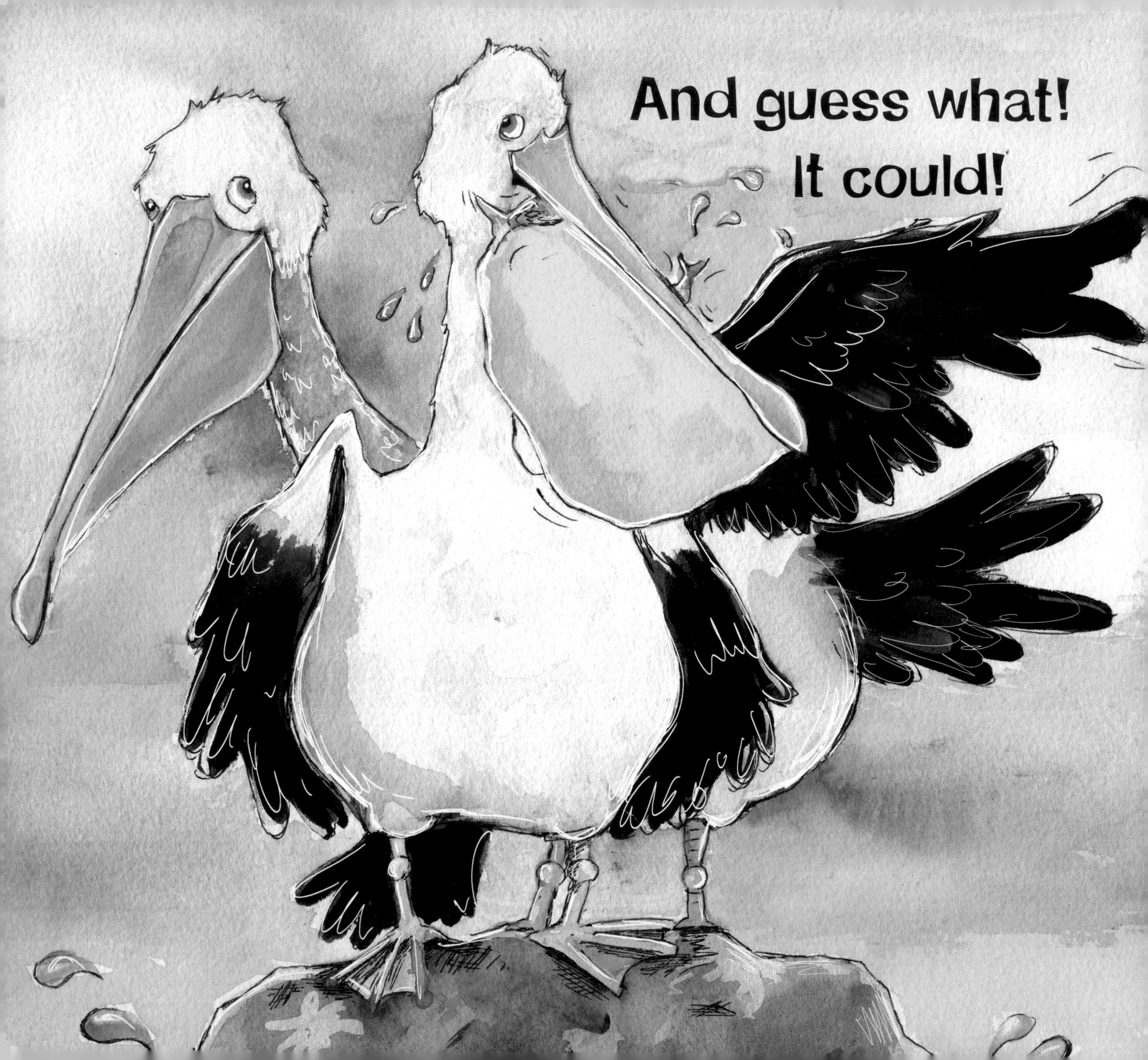

"Well, if you can eat them, I could
eat at least one hundred starfish."
"But they will squirm and writhe,"
replied the other pelican.
"Well, just watch."

"No, you can't."
"Yes, I can."
"Can't."
"Can."

And guess what!
It could!

"Well, if you managed that, I could easily eat that pod of lobsters."

"But they will pinch and snap," replied the other pelican.

"Well, here goes."

"No, you can't."

"Yes, I can."

"Can't."

"Can."

And guess what!
It could!

"Right, well I'll show you. I can eat a
whole swarm of jellyfish all in one go!"
"But they will wobble and quiver,"
replied the other pelican.
"Well, take a look at this."

"No, you can't."
"Yes, I can."
"Can't."
"Can."

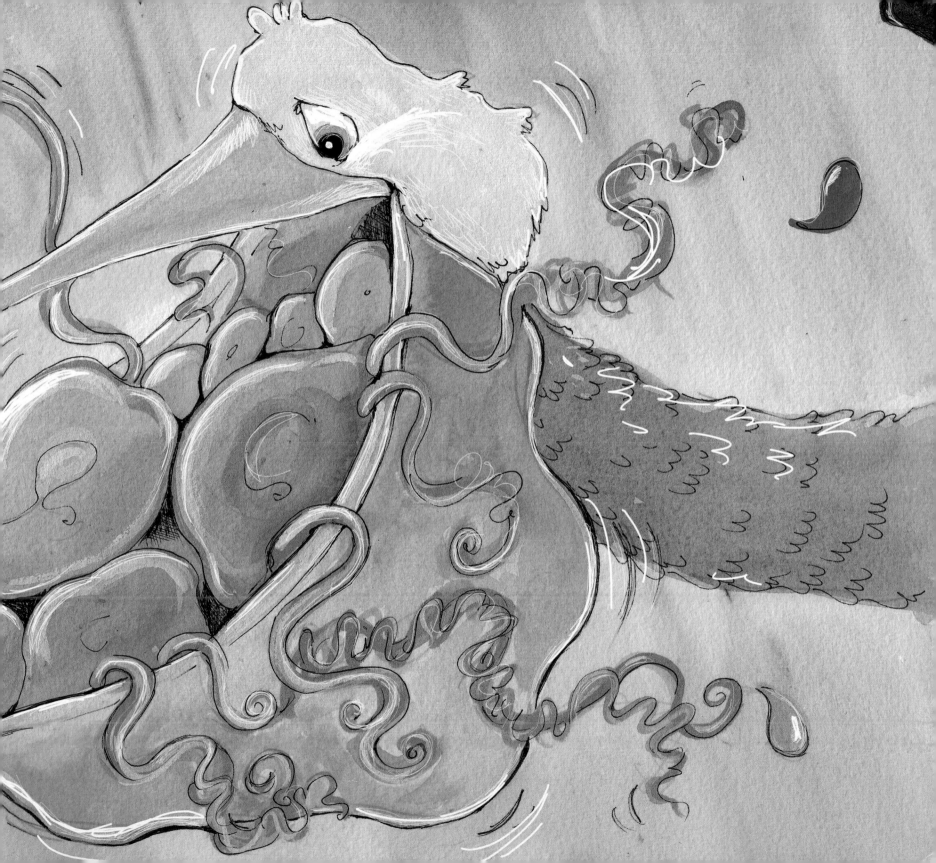

And guess what!
It could!

And guess what!
It could!

"I can outdo that. I can eat a giant eel all in one go!"
"But it will thrash and splash!" replied the other pelican.
"Well, as if that will stop me!"

"No, you can't."
"Yes, I can."
"Can't."
"Can."

"If you can do that, then I could eat
a whole school of squids!"
"But they will suck and slither,"
replied the other pelican.
"Do I look as if I care?"

"No, you can't."
"Yes, I can."
"Can't."
"Can."

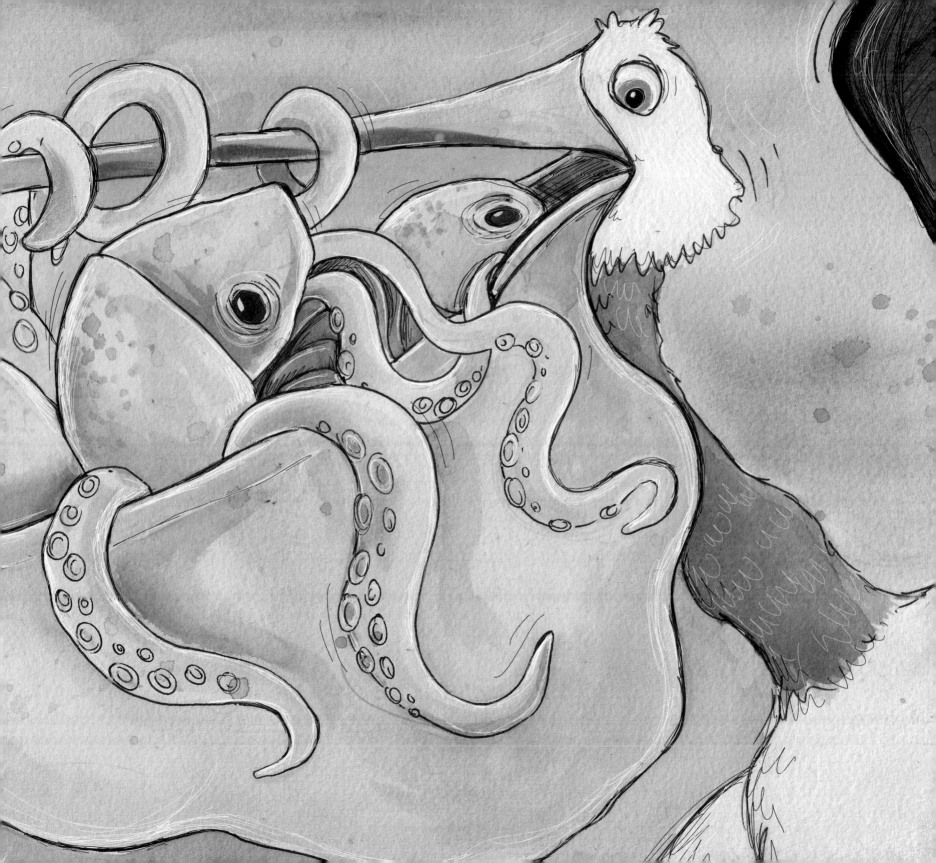

And guess what!
It could!

"Well, outdo this if you can. I could eat that shark all in one go!"
"No, don't be silly. It will tear and twist," replied the other pelican.
"As if that will stop me."

"But, you can't."
"Yes, I can."
"But you shouldn't."
"Yes, I should."
"But you mustn't."
"Yes, I will."

But it couldn't ...

Now there is one pelican left sitting on a rock and it isn't feeling hungry at all.

(And in future it's sticking to pilchards!)